QUILTS
coloring book

Maybe you've had the pleasure of taking a nap under a patchwork quilt, enjoying its bright colors and dazzling patterns as well as its warmth. Quilts are often made by piecing together cloth shapes to create a quilt top, adding warm cotton batting and a backing cloth, and then sewing the three layers together with decorative needlework. This technique of piecing together bits of cloth allows for an almost endless variety of colors and patterns and often produces stunning designs.

Quiltmaking is a traditional American craft. To this day small groups of women gather, needles and thread in hand, to stitch quilts—strengthening bonds of friendship and community while they create vividly colorful and unique bedcovers. Most of the quilts in this coloring book were made by women in the eastern and midwestern United States sometime between the mid-1800s and mid-1900s. As you color in the outlines, take a moment to think about the women who stitched these quilts with love, precision, and creativity. Their intention was to protect their families from the winter chill and delight them at the same time.

The 22 quilts in this coloring book are shown as small pictures on the inside front and back covers. You might want to copy the original colors, or you might decide to use your own. We've left the last page of the book blank so that you can design and color a quilt of your own.

AMERICAN FOLK ART MUSEUM

Pomegranate Kids®

All drawings are adapted from quilts in the collection of the American Folk Art Museum, New York. Photographs by Gavin Ashworth, New York (1–6, 8, 11, 13, 14, 16, 17, 19), John Parnell, New York (7), Matt Hoebermann, New York (9, 10), Schecter Lee, New York (15, 22), Scott Bowron, New York (20), and unidentified photographers (12, 18, 21).

1. *Carpenter's Wheel Quilt,* artist unidentified, Pennsylvania, 1835–1845. Cotton, 102¼ x 101¼ in. Gift of Cyril Irwin Nelson, 1992.28.2.

2. *Surprise Quilt Presented to Mary A. Grow,* various quiltmakers, Plymouth, Michigan, 1856. Cotton with ink and embroidery, 87 x 82½ in. Gift in memory of Margaret Trautwein Stoddard and her daughter, Eleanor Stoddard Seibold, 2003.2.1.

3. *Cookie Cutter Quilt,* artist unidentified, probably Pennsylvania, 1875–1925. Cotton, 79½ x 71¾ in. Gift of Dr. Stanley and Jacqueline Schneider, 1979.21.1.

4. *Strawberries in Pots Quilt,* artist unidentified, possibly Missouri, 1850–1860. Cotton, 91 x 89 in. Gift of Phyllis Haders, 1981.18.1.

5. *Cross and Block Quilt,* artist unidentified, possibly New York State, Pennsylvania, or Ontario, 1880–1900. Wool, 71 x 76 in. Gift of Mr. and Mrs. Alan Weinstein, 2007.15.5.

6. *Floral Crib Quilt,* artist unidentified, United States, 1850–1880. Cotton, 46 x 39 in. Gift of Cyril Irwin Nelson, 1998.13.2.

7. *Reiter Family Album Quilt,* artist unidentified, descended in the family of Katie Friedman Reiter (1873–1942) and Liebe Gross Friedman (dates unknown), probably Baltimore, 1848–1850. Cotton and wool, 101 x 101 in. Gift of Katherine Amelia Wine in honor of her grandmother Theresa Reiter Gross and the makers of the quilt, her great-grandmother Katie Friedman Reiter and her great-great-grandmother Liebe Gross Friedman, and on behalf of a generation of cousins: Sydney Howard Reiter, Penelope Breyer Tarplin, Jonnie Breyer Stahl, Susan Reiter Blinn, Benjamin Joseph Gross, and Leba Gross Wine, 2000.2.1.

8. *Pennsylvania Hex Quilt,* artist unidentified, United States, 1860–1900. Cotton, 94 x 100 in. Gift of David L. Davies, 1997.4.2.

9. *Floral Medallion Quilt,* artist unidentified, possibly Vincennes, Indiana, 1870–1880. Cotton, 86 x 70 in. Gift of Irene Reichert, 1993.1.3.

10. *Lone Star Quilt,* Amanda Yoder (dates unknown) and her daughter Anna (dates unknown), Honeyville, Indiana, 1925–1940. Cotton, 79 x 75½ in. Gift of David Pottinger, 1980.37.57.

11. *Log Cabin Quilt, Barn Raising Variation,* unidentified Mennonite artist, Ohio, 1950–1960. Cotton, wool, and rayon, 85½ x 73¼ in. Gift of Mr. and Mrs. Alan Weinstein, 2007.15.9.

12. *Stars and Pentagons Quilt,* artist unidentified, United States, 1880–1900. Silk, 81 x 44 in. (framed). Gift of Jacqueline L. Fowler, 1981.2.1.

13. *Log Cabin Throw, Light and Dark Variation,* Harriet Rutter Eagleson (1855–c. 1925), New York City, 1874–1880. Silk and cotton, 57¾ x 57¾ in. Gift of Miss Jessica R. Eagleson, 1979.18.1.

14. *Star of Bethlehem Quilt,* artist unidentified, possibly Sullivan County, New York, 1880–1900. Silk, 99 x 94¼ in. Purchase made possible with funds from the Great American Quilt Festival 2, 1990.15.1.

15. *Hummingbirds Quilt,* artist unidentified, Shipshewana, Indiana, 1920–1930. Cotton, 87¾ x 68¼ in. (framed). Gift of David Pottinger, 1980.37.69.

16. *Holly Hocks Quilt,* Eva G. Rex (dates unknown), United States, 1944. Cotton, 96 x 81 in. Gift of Cyril Irwin Nelson, 2004.14.5.

17. *Star of France Quilt,* artist unidentified, United States, 1930–1940. Cotton, 81¾ x 81¾ in. Gift of Cyril Irwin Nelson in honor of Robert Bishop, American Folk Art Museum director (1977–1991), 1990.17.4.

18. *Four-Patch and Triangles Quilt,* Barbara Zook Peachey (1848–1930), Mifflin County, Pennsylvania, Yellow Topper Amish, Byler Group, 1910–1920. Cotton, 85½ x 78¾ in. Gift of Mr. and Mrs. William B. Wigton, 1984.25.12.

19. *Sixteen-Patch Variation Quilt,* artist unidentified, Kalona, Iowa, 1950–1960. Cotton, 92 x 86 in. Gift of Mr. and Mrs. Alan Weinstein, 2007.15.6.

20. *Star Quilt,* Nora McKeown Ezell (1917–2007), Eutaw, Alabama, 1977. Cotton and synthetics, 94 x 84 in. Purchase made possible in part by a grant from the National Endowment for the Arts, with matching funds from the Great American Quilt Festival 3, 1991.13.1.

21. *Fans Quilt,* artist unidentified, initialed "PM," Indiana, 1925–1935. Cotton, wool, and rayon with cotton embroidery, 82 x 71½ in. Gift of David Pottinger, 1980.37.86.

22. *Double Wedding Ring Quilt,* artist unidentified, United States, 1940–1950. Cotton and muslin, 82 x 81 in. Gift of Robert Bishop, 1993.4.14.

Pomegranate Communications, Inc.
19018 NE Portal Way, Portland OR 97230
800 227 1428   www.pomegranate.com

© 2010 American Folk Art Museum, New York
Line drawings © Pomegranate Communications, Inc.

Item No. CB127

Designed and rendered by Oky Sulistio

Printed in Korea

23 22 21 20 19 18 17 16 15 14   11 10 9 8 7 6 5 4 3 2

Pomegranate Europe Ltd.
Unit 1, Heathcote Business Centre, Hurlbutt Road
Warwick, Warwickshire CV34 6TD, UK
[+44] 0 1926 430111
sales@pomeurope.co.uk

This product is in compliance with the Consumer Product Safety Improvement Act of 2008 (CPSIA). A General Conformity Certificate concerning Pomegranate's compliance with the CPSIA is available on our website at www.pomegranate.com, or by request at 800 227 1428. For additional CPSIA-required tracking details, contact Pomegranate at 800 227 1428.

1. *Carpenter's Wheel Quilt* (detail)

2. *Surprise Quilt Presented to Mary A. Grow* (detail)

3. *Cookie Cutter Quilt* (detail)

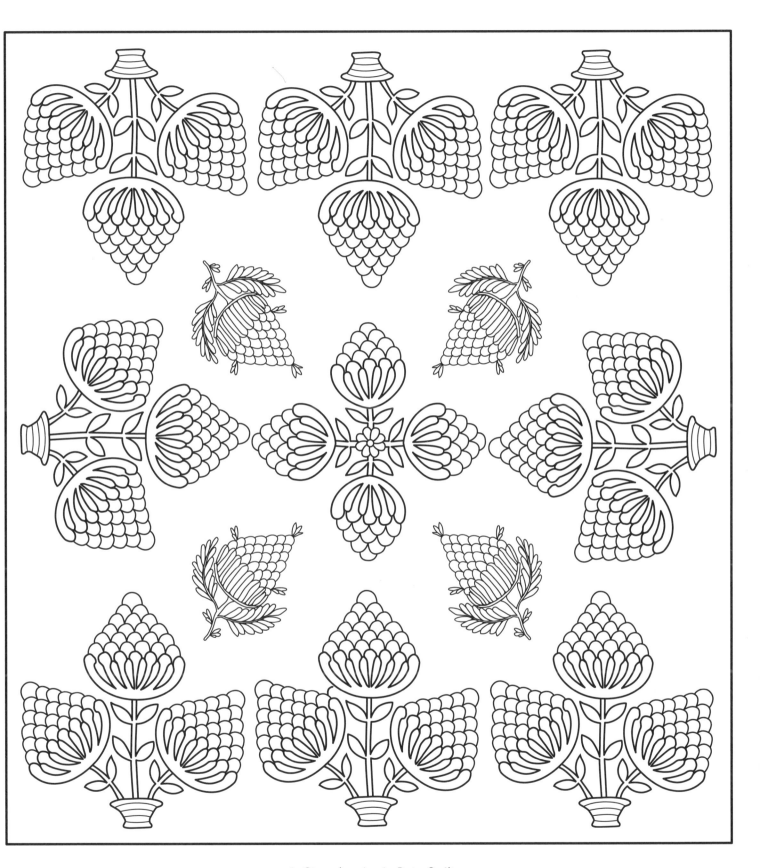

4. Strawberries in Pots Quilt

5. *Cross and Block Quilt* (detail)

6. *Floral Crib Quilt*

7. *Reiter Family Album Quilt* (detail)

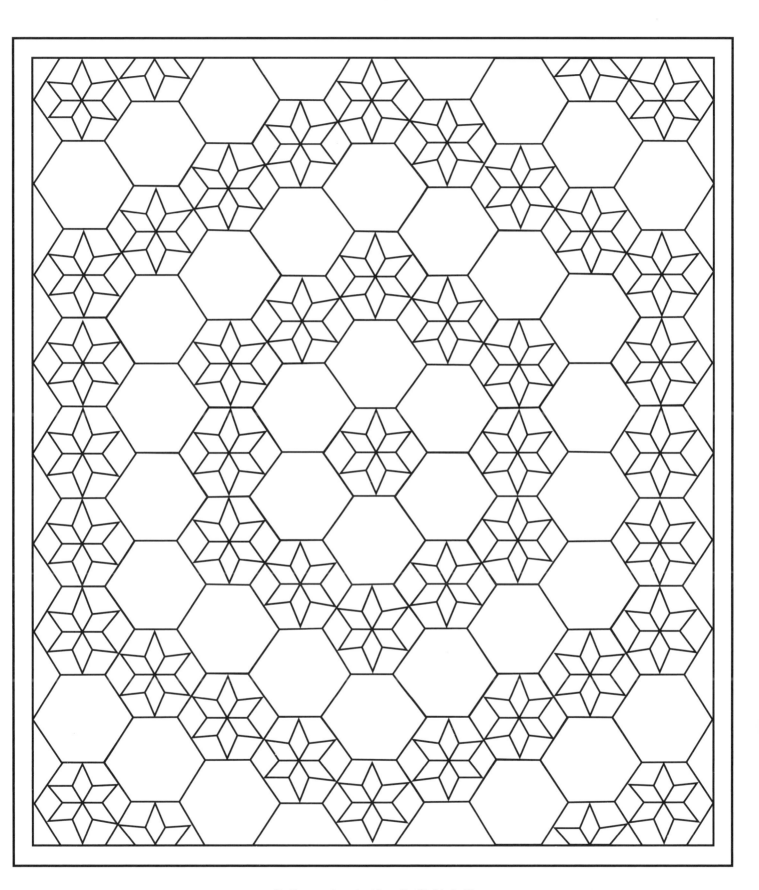

8. *Pennsylvania Hex Quilt* (detail)

9. Floral Medallion Quilt

10. *Lone Star Quilt* (detail)

11. *Log Cabin Quilt, Barn Raising Variation* (detail)

12. *Stars and Pentagons Quilt* (detail)

13. *Log Cabin Throw, Light and Dark Variation* (detail)

14. *Star of Bethlehem Quilt* (detail)

15. *Hummingbirds Quilt* (detail)

16. *Holly Hocks Quilt*

17. *Star of France Quilt* (detail)

18. *Four-Patch and Triangles Quilt*

19. *Sixteen-Patch Variation Quilt* (detail)

20. *Star Quilt*

21. *Fans Quilt* (detail)

22. *Double Wedding Ring Quilt* (detail)

Draw and color your own quilt here!

Draw and color your own quilt here!